Simplified Piano Solo

THE WORLD'S GREAT CLASSICAL MUSIC

Opera's Greatest Melodies

71 Favorite Selections from 42 Operas

Transcribed for Simplified Piano Solo / Lower Intermediate Level

EDITED BY BLAKE NEELY AND RICHARD WALTERS

Cover Painting: Degas, *The Song of the Dog*, 1876

ISBN 0-634-00554-5

HAL•LEONARD®
CORPORATION

7777 W. BLUEMOUND RD. P.O. BOX 13819 MILWAUKEE, WI 53213

Visit Hal Leonard Online at
www.halleonard.com

C O N T E N T S

ABOUT THE OPERAS...

AÏDA (1871).
Music by Giuseppe Verdi. Libretto by Antonio Ghislanzoni. Verdi's most popular opera is set in ancient Egypt. Aïda is an Ethiopian princess who has been captured and enslaved by the royal court in Egypt, at war with Ethiopia. She is in love with Radames, leader of the Egyptian army against her people. Amneris, princess of Egypt is also in love with Radames. Near the beginning of the opera we hear Radames' feelings for Aïda in the aria "Celeste Aïda" (Radiant Aïda). The "Triumphal March" is the center of a lavish scene at the Egyptian royal court celebrating Radames' victory over the Ethiopian army. It is one of the grandest scenes in all of opera. Later in the story Radames reveals military plans of the Egyptian army to Aïda, who is desperate to save her country from capture. He is accused of treason, and doomed to die in a sealed temple. Aïda hides in the temple to die with her beloved.

IL BARBIERE DI SIVIGLIA (The Barber of Seville) (1816).
Music by Gioachino Rossini. Libretto by Cesare Sterbini (adapted from the play by Beaumarchais, *Le Barbier de Seville*). The comic opera is set in 17th century Seville, but is usually played as the 18th century. Rosina is a ward of Bartolo, an elderly gentleman with intentions of marrying the beautiful young woman. Count Almaviva disguises himself as a student (Lindoro) to court Rosina. The crafty Figaro, a barber, comes to the aid of Almaviva in his pursuit. Rosina has received letters from Almaviva, whom she believes to be Lindoro. In the charming aria "Una voce poco fa" she describes how she has the necessary qualities to escape Bartolo's plans to marry her. She vows that, "Lindoro will be mine." It works. With Figaro's help they confound Bartolo, and at the end Rosina discovers she has fallen in love with a Count.

LA BOHÈME (The Bohemian Life) (1896).
Music by Giacomo Puccini. Libretto by Giuseppe Giacosa and Luigi Illica (adapted from the novel by Henri Murger). The story is set in Paris in 1830, although the opera is often played in the period of its composition, the 1890s. Rodolfo is a starving poet, roommate to the painter Marcello. They have two good friends in the musician Schaunard and the philosopher Colline. On Christmas Eve Rodolfo sends his friends out for the evening while he tries to finish an article for a deadline. Mimi, a neighbor in the apartment building, knocks on his door and asks if he will light her candle. Immediately the two are attracted to one another. Mimi drops her key (accidentally?). Rodolfo's candle blows out (accidentally?). They look for her key in the dark. In the aria "Che gelida manina" (How cold your little hand is) he poetically describes himself and his life to Mimi. By the end of act one the couple is in love, as we hear in the duet "O soave fanciulla." They join Rodolfo's friends at the busy Cafe Momus. The dramatic and coquettish cafe singer Musetta, former lover of Marcello, arrives, and draws attention to herself (especially Marcello's attention) by bursting into song in "Quando men vo." Rodolfo and Mimi later quarrel and split, just as Marcello and Musetta patch things up. Mimi becomes ill with consumption. Musetta brings her back to the garrett shared by Rodolfo and Marcello. Mimi and Rodolfo renew their love for one another. Her "death aria" is "Sono andati." She dies, with all the Bohemian friends present, and with Rodolfo sobbing over her body.

CARMEN (1875).
Music by Georges Bizet. Libretto by Henri Meilhac and Ludovic Halévy (adapted from the novel by Prosper Mérimée). The opera takes place in Spain. Carmen is a free-thinking, independent gypsy girl who is temporarily working in a cigarette factory in Seville. The women workers take a work break, and all the men around wait outside with hopes of meeting the alluring Carmen. She enters, singing the famous "Habanera," in which she states her personal theories of love: don't try to hold me; if you don't love me, I'll fall for you, and you had better watch out! She gets into a fight with a co-worker, and is arrested. While being guarded by Don José she seduces him in her aria "Seguidilla," in which she describes the good life the two of them can share together. Later in the story, Carmen is dazzled by the famous bull fighter Escamillo. He describes his thrilling encounters facing the bull in the "Toreador Song." Don José has fallen in love with Carmen, and comes to the inn where she is staying. He tells her his feelings in the "Flower Song" (La fleur que tu mavais je t'aime). He saved the flower she tossed him, and has become obsessed with her. She teases him, and says if he really loved her he would abandon his position in the army and come away with her. He reluctantly deserts his post, and becomes part of the gypsy band of smugglers with her. She grows tired of him, and starts a romance with Escamillo. At the end of the opera, a desperately jealous Don José kills Carmen, rather than see her with another man.

CAVALLERIA RUSTICANA (Rustic Chivalry) (1890).
Music by Pietro Mascagni. Libretto by Giovanni Targioni-Tozzetti and Guido Menasci. This short opera is often played in a double bill with *I Pagliacci*. The setting is Easter Sunday in a Sicilian village. Turridu returned to his native village and took up with Santuzza, who is now pregnant with his child. But he is still in love with his former lover, Lola, who married Alfio, and begins an adulterous affair with her. Turridu abandons Santuzza, who in bitterness tells Alfio of Lola and Turridu. At this point in the opera there is an instrumental interlude, an intermezzo, that compacts the sad emotions of the story, and sets up the opera's tragic ending. Alfio challenges Turridu to a duel. Turridu sings a sad farewell to his mother, then is killed by Alfio.

LES CONTES D'HOFFMANN (The Tales of Hoffmann) (1881).
Music by Jacques Offenbach. Libretto by Jules Barbier and Michel Carré (based on stories of E.T.A. Hoffmann). Offenbach was famous as a composer of comic operettas, but at the end of his life he did what no one expected from him in writing an expansive, serious opera. He died during the rehearsals, and *Les Contes d'Hoffmann* was orchestrated and completed by several other composers. The opera's prologue begins in a beer-cellar in Nuremberg. The poet Hoffmann drinks with companions, and as they drink, he tells them three tales of his tragic love life, which comprise the three acts of the opera. Act II of the opera is set in Venice, and the famous "Barcarolle" begins the act with music that evokes the canals and gondoliers of that romantic city.

DIDO AND AENEAS (1689).

Music by Henry Purcell. Libretto by Nahum Tate (adapted from Virgil's *Aeneid*). This was arguably the first through-sung opera written in the English language. The setting is Carthage after the Trojan War. Dido, queen of Carthage, and Aeneas, a Trojan, have fallen in love with one another. Aeneas is tricked by witches disguised as the god Mercury, commanding him to depart and set out to make a new Troy. Dido is inconsolable at his departure, and sings "When I am laid in earth" as she faces her suicide at a funeral pyre.

DON GIOVANNI (1787).

Music by Wolfgang Amadeus Mozart. Libretto by Lorenzo Da Ponte. This tragic-comic opera is loosely based on the legends of Don Juan (as well as an Italian play, *The Stone Guest*). Don Giovanni is a dashing Spanish nobleman who seduces women for sport. (His servant, Leporello, tells us that in Spain alone he has seduced 1,003 women!) The opera is set in Seville in the 17th century (but most productions play it as the 18th century). Don Giovanni steals into the bedroom of Donna Anna and attempts to seduce her. Her father, the Commendatore, enters, and Don Giovanni kills him. Donna Anna and her fiancé, Don Ottavio, pursue Don Giovanni for justice and vengeance throughout the rest of the opera. He has also seduced Donna Elvira, who has fallen in love with him, much to her misfortune. She pursues him. Giovanni is unbothered by these pursuits. He comes upon a lovely peasant girl, Zerlina, who is about to be married to Masetto. That doesn't stop him, and he very nearly seduces her in the duet "Là ci darem la mano." The Minuet, included in this collection, is dance music from a scene in Don Giovanni's palace, a ball he is hosting in honor of Zerlina and Masetto's marriage. Actually, his attention is yet another seduction attempt with the girl. Giovanni later beats up Masetto. Zerlina consoles her fiancé, healing his emotional and physical wounds in the lovely aria "Vedrai, carino." The opera ends when the statue of the murdered Commendatore comes to life, demanding that Don Giovanni repent his sins. The Don refuses, and is dragged into the fiery pit of hell.

L'ELISIR D'AMORE (The Elixir of Love) (1832).

Music by Gaetano Donizetti. Libretto by Felice Romani. The setting for this comedy is an Italian village. Nemorino is a peasant, in love with Adina, a rich young woman who owns a large estate. Nemorino is persuaded by Dulcamara, a quack, to buy a "love potion" that will make him irresistible to the girls, including Adina. Nemorino becomes drunk from the "potion" and Adina is so put off that she agrees to marry Belcore. Meanwhile, all the village learns that Nemorino is to inherit great wealth from a rich uncle. But Nemorino doesn't yet know this. All the girls adore him, which he credits to his potion. Adina becomes jealous of his attentions to others. Nemorino is hurt by her harsh words, and in despair sings "Una furtiva lagrima." She later declares her feelings for him. It's a happy ending when they are betrothed.

EUGENE ONEGIN (1879).

Music by Pyotr Il'yich Tchaikovsky. Libretto by Konstantin Shilovsky and Tchaikovsky (adapted from a dramatic poem by Pushkin). The opera takes place in Russia, c. 1800. Eugene Onegin is a malcontent aristocrat. Tatiana falls in love with him, but he tells her he cannot give her his heart, only his friendship. Onegin later flirts with Olga, Tatiana's sister. Olga is engaged to Lenski, a poet and great friend of Onegin. Lenski challenges Onegin to a duel. Before the duel Lenski sings this haunting lament ("Lenski's Aria"). He is killed in the duel by Onegin. Onegin hates his life and begs Tatiana to accept his love, but she is now married to Prince Gremin, and rejects him.

FAUST (1859).

Music by Charles Gounod. Libretto by Jules Barbier and Michel Carré (adapted from the drama by Goethe). The opera takes place in a 16th century German village. Faust, an elderly philosopher, sells his soul to the devil (Méphistophélès) in exchange for youth and the beautiful young Marguerite, who was revealed to him in a vision and with whom he is in love. Faust contemplates her as he stands outside her house singing the aria "Salut! demeure chaste et pure" (Hail, dwelling chaste and pure). She falls in love with the now young Faust. Marguerite's brother, Valentin, returns from war, and challenges Faust to a duel when he realizes his sister's virginity has been robbed by Faust. Valentin is killed. Marguerite and Faust split up, and she delivers his son, kills the infant in shame, and is sentenced to death. She goes insane in prison. Méphistophélèles and Faust go to Marguerite's prison cell. She denies her love for Faust and dies. The devil condemns her to hell, but angels appear and take her to heaven.

LA FAVORITA (The Favorite Woman) (1840).

Music by Gaetano Donizetti. Libretto by Alphonse Royer, Gustave Vaëz, and Eugene Scribe. Though this opera was written in French and premiered in Paris, it has remained in the repertoire in an Italian translation first performed in 1895. The setting is Castile, Spain, 1340. Fernando is in training to become a monk. He falls in love with Leonora, whom he doesn't realize is actually mistress to the King of Castile. Leonora persuades the King to grant Fernando an appointment in the army. He saves the King's life and wins a battle. For reward he asks for Leonora's hand in marriage. The married King cannot publicly acknowledge his adulterous affair with Leonora (for he would be excommunicated), and grants Fernando's wish. Fernando discovers the truth after the marriage, and in shock and shame leaves Leonora and returns to the monastery. Before taking his final vows to become a monk Leonora comes to visit him. He remembers his love for her and sings the famous aria "Spirto gentil." She collapses with emotion and dies.

FEDORA (1898).

Music by Umberto Giordano. Libretto by Arturo Colautti (adapted from a play by Sardou). This murder mystery opera takes place in St. Petersburg, Paris and Switzerland. Fedora Romanov is a Russian princess. Loris Ipanov killed her fiancé because his wife had an affair with him. Ipanov falls in love with the glamorous Fedora, and in the famous "encore aria," "Amor ti vieta," he declares his love to her. Fedora schemes vengeance, but eventually falls in love with Ipanov when she learns his true motive for the killing. Ipanov's family falls on hard times, and he learns that an unidentified woman is to blame. It was actually Fedora's schemes coming to fruition, but she couldn't stop them after falling in love with Ipanov. She realizes that Ipanov will discover that she brought hardship on his family, and she poisons herself. Ipanov understands all, but only when it is too late.

DIE FLEDERMAUS (The Bat) (1874).
Music by Johann Strauss, Jr. Libretto by Carl Haffner and Richard Genée. This sparkling operetta is set in Vienna. Strauss, famous for his waltzes, put one of his best in the overture, "The Fledermaus Waltz." The plot involves Dr. Falke's revenge on his friend Gabriel von Eisenstein. Before the action of the opera Falke had been to a costume ball dressed as a bat, and drank a bit too much. Eisenstein put him on a bench in a popular park for the night, and Falke woke to be the laughing stock of passersby. He swears to get even with his friend's practical joke. The resulting plot is an intricate comedy, but the basic idea is that Eisenstein, at yet another costume ball, unknowingly courts his costumed wife, Rosalinde, thinking she is a Hungarian princess. There is a tangle of a climax, but all ends happily. The score is rich with lovely melodies. Act II of the opera takes place at a ball hosted by the young Russian Prince Orlofsky, who is blasé about everything. He sings the aria "Chacun à son goût" (Each to his own), expressing his laissez-faire philosophy of life. (Most productions invite "guests" to the party scene, and might interpolate practically anything, from circus acts to jazz singers.)

GIANNI SCHICCHI (1918).
Music by Giacomo Puccini. Libretto by Giovacchino Forzano. This one-act comic opera is part three of *Il trittico* (The Trilogy). The setting is Florence, 1299. The old and wealthy Buoso Donati is dying, and his relatives gather around in false mourning, actually waiting to see what they get in the old man's will. They are outraged when they discover the will and read that Donati has left his estate to a monastery. Rinuccio, one of the young nephews, is in love with Lauretta, daughter of Gianni Schicchi. His family will not approve his wedding plans with her because they feel she is not worthy of them. Rinuccio is the one who finds the will, but before he hands it over, he makes them promise they will allow the crafty Gianni Schicchi to help them out of their predicament, and also allow his marriage plans. In Rinuccio's aria he sings of the glories of Florence's past, and paints Gianni Schicchi as another in a long line of the city's noble citizens. Schicchi arrives but is reluctant to help the greedy relatives. His daughter, in love with Rinuccio, pleads with him in the famous aria "O mio babbino caro." He relents, and plays a trick on the family. He poses as Donati, they hide the still warm body, and Schicchi dictates a new will, with a lawyer present, in which he leaves himself most of the estate.

GIULIO CESARE (Julius Caesar) (1724).
Music by George Frideric Handel. Libretto by Nicola F. Haym. The full original title is *Giulio Cesare in Egitto* (Julius Caesar in Egypt). Handel's operas were popular in their time, but fell from the repertoire for over 200 years, to be revived by opera companies frequently in the 1960s, 1970s, and especially the 1980s and 1990s. (*Giulio Cesare* was the opera that made a star of Beverly Sills in 1966.) The opera is set in Egypt in 48 B.C. There is a tangled plot of political intrigue and romance. Cleopatra, queen of Egypt, and her brother, King Ptolemy, competing for power in Egypt, vie for the favor of the visiting Julius Caesar, ruler of Rome. Cleopatra uses her feminine beauty and sex appeal to lure Caesar, having a decided advantage over her brother. At one point in the story Cleopatra is imprisoned by her brother. She believes that her beloved Caesar is dead. She sings the beautiful lament "Piangeò la sorte mia," with a stormy middle section in which she describes a vision of herself returning as a ghost to haunt her evil brother. Caesar triumphs, is united (for the time being) with Cleopatra, and the opera ends happily. (The story stops before the later events, such as Cleopatra's self-inflicted poisonous snake bites.)

GUILLAUME TELL (William Tell) (1829).
Music by Gioachino Rossini. Libretto by Étienne de Jouy, Hippolyte-Louis-Florent Bis, and Armand Marrast (adapted from the German play by Schiller). This was Rossini's last opera. After over 15 years of being the most successful opera composer in Europe, he shocked everyone and retired from opera composition at the age of 37. The opera (in French — it was commissioned from Paris Opéra and premiered there) is set in Switzerland in the 13th century. William Tell is a Swiss patriot, a rebel to the Austrian conquerors of his country. He helps someone escape capture from the Austrian troops, and is himself captured, along with his son, Jemmy. Tell is forced, with bow and arrow, to shoot an apple placed on his son's head. It's right on target, leaving the boy unharmed. But Tell makes the mistake of telling his captor, the Austrian governor Gessler, that if he had wounded his son with the arrow, that he would have immediately aimed an arrow at the governor. Tell is arrested, but escapes and leads the Swiss in a victorious revolt against the Austrian army. The opera is a rarity, but the overture is world-famous, especially as "The Lone Ranger Theme."

HMS PINAFORE (1878).
Music by Arthur Sullivan. Libretto by W.S. Gilbert. The subtitle of this favorite Gilbert & Sullivan operetta is "The Lass That Loved a Sailor." The action opens on the ship Pinafore, in anchor at Portsmouth, full of sailors. The popular but lovelorn Mrs. Cripps (known as Little Buttercup) comes down to the dock to greet them, with many temptations for the sailors to purchase. Ralph Rackstraw, one of the seamen, is in love with the captain's daughter, Josephine. Captain Corcoran, commander of the Pinafore, has arranged a marriage for his daughter with Sir Joseph Porter (an arrogant jerk), First Lord of the Admirality. Josephine is completely unenthusiastic at the prospect, and prefers her common sailor beloved, Ralph, even though she will miss the comforts a richer husband could afford. The captain is warned by the deadbeat sailor Dick Deadeye that Josephine plans to elope with Ralph Rackstraw. (Even his name seems to describe the only kind of wedding bed he could afford.) Sir Joseph overhears the Captain's exasperation at his daughter's plans, and he confines him to quarters because he forgets his manners and uses a mild obscenity (very mild and G-rated). Sir Joseph stops the eloping lovers and sentences Ralph to the ship's dungeon. Then Little Buttercup reveals the surprise ending. Once upon a time she looked after two babies, one a little lordling, and the other a common peasant. She realizes now that she mixed them up. "The well-born babe was Ralph Rackstraw, and your Captain was the other!" Since noble birth is the most important thing (this was one of the satirical operetta's comic points), Ralph was immediately made captain of the Pinafore by the snobby Sir Joseph, and Captain Corcoran was stripped of his rank. And since he was now a common seaman, Sir Joseph was no longer interested in marrying his daughter, Josephine. Ralph winds up with Josephine, Corcoran winds up with Little Buttercup, and Sir Joseph is swept up by his annoying but aristocratic relatives.

HÄNSEL UND GRETEL (Hansel and Gretel) (1893).

Music by Engelbert Humperdinck. Libretto by Adelheid Wette (adapted from the Grimm brothers' story). This enchanting fairy-tale opera takes place "once upon a time" in the Harz Mountains, near the mysterious Mount Ilsenstein. A poor family lives in the deep forest, father Peter, mother Gertrude, and their two children, Hansel and Gretel. Gertrude sends the two children out to pick strawberries in the woods, but they get lost. In the deep, dark forest they resign themselves to their state, and prepare to go to sleep. Their fears are calmed by the "Evening Prayer." As the children sleep fourteen angels come down from heaven to protect them. In the morning they stumble on a gingerbread house, and are captured by the evil witch who lives there. She casts a magic spell on them, locks Hansel in a cage and force feeds him so that he will fatten up before she eats him, and forces Gretel to cook and clean. Hansel and Gretel outsmart the witch, and shove her into the huge oven. The other children captured by the witch's spell are freed. Peter and Gertrude have been desperately looking for their children, and arrive just after the witch is cooked. All rejoice in reunion and say a prayer of thanks.

LOUISE (1900).

Music and libretto by Gustave Charpentier. There was never a more Parisian opera than *Louise*. The setting is Paris, and the opera incorporates realistic, ordinary settings, including a huge cast of Bohemian artists and working people. The story is of Louise, a young woman from the working class, who leaves her conservative parents to live in Monmartre with Julien, an idealistic artist and liberal social activist. (He is passionate for what are basically socialistic ideals.) The languorous aria "Depuis le jour" is sung by Louise at twilight just outside the small house she is sharing with Julien. The opening line can be translated "Since the day I gave myself to you..." It is definitely sensual music. Her mother comes to her to tell her that her father is seriously ill and wants to see her. Louise returns to her parents. Her father recovers and forbids her to return to Julien, but after a time Louise proclaims her right to be free as an individual to do as she pleases (she's been influenced by Julien's causes). Her father throws her out of the house, cursing Paris and the spell it has cast on his daughter.

LUCIA DI LAMMERMOOR (Lucia of Lammermoor) (1835).

Music by Gaetano Donizetti. Libretto by Salvatore Cammarano (adapted from the novel by Walter Scott, *The Bride of Lammermoor*). The setting is Scotland, c. 1700. Donizetti's most beloved *bel canto* tragedy is the tale of two Scottish feuding families, Lucy Ashton (the character's name is Lucia in the Italian version of the story for the opera) is in love with Edgar of Ravenswood (adapted to Edgardo for the opera). Her brother, Lord Henry Ashton (Enrico in the opera) has fallen on hard times, and to replenish his fortune he has arranged a marriage for Lucia to Lord Arthur Bucklaw (Arturo in the opera). Lucia knows nothing of this plan. Enrico knows nothing of Lucia's love of his arch rival, Edgardo. Edgardo is called away to France. While he is gone, Lucia is reluctantly persuaded by Edgardo to sign the marriage contract with Arturo. Just after she has signed, Edgardo appears, convinced she has willingly betrayed his love for her. At this dramatic moment comes the famous sextet, where each character expresses his or her distress in the situation (Lucia, her companion Alisa, Arturo, Enrico, Edgardo, and Raimondo, chaplain of the estate). Enrico and Edgardo agree to fight a duel. Lucia, a fragile young woman, goes suddenly insane at the strain, and stabs her new husband, Arturo, whom she detests. She collapses and dies. When Edgardo hears of Lucia's death, he stabs himself.

MADAMA BUTTERFLY (Madame Butterfly) (1904).

Music by Giacomo Puccini. Libretto by Giuseppe Giacosa and Luigi Illica (adapted from the play by David Belasco). The opera takes place in Nagasaki, c. 1900. An American sailor, Lieutenant B.F. Pinkerton, is stationed in Japan for a time. To have female companionship during his temporary stay in Japan, he arranges a "Japanese marriage" to a Geisha through a marriage broker to a 15-year-old girl, Cio-Cio San, called Butterfly. She is dressed in a Japanese wedding gown, accompanied by many female friends and attendants, and makes one of the most spectacularly beautiful entrances in opera. ("Entrance of Butterfly" is included in this collection). Though he is very romantic with Butterfly, especially in the love duet scene of their first night together, Pinkerton doesn't take the relationship seriously, and plans to marry a "real wife" upon returning to the U.S. Cio-Cio San falls in love with him. After a time his ship sails. Cio-Cio San waits for him, now with Pinkerton's son she has born. Everyone else knows the truth, but she insists that Pinkerton will return to her, expressed in the aria "Un bel dì vedremo." In fact, Pinkerton does return, with his American wife, to take his son back to his country. When he arrives at Cio-Cio San's house she is out. He sees the cruelty of what he has done, and sings a sincere farewell to the house in the aria "Addio, fiorito asil." He leaves. Butterfly rushes in, expecting to see him, but then learns the harsh truth, especially in facing Kate Pinkerton, the real wife. Butterfly then stabs herself with her father's sword and dies.

MANON (1884).

Music by Jules Massenet. Libretto by Henri Meilhac and Philippe Gille. This opera is set in France of the early 18th century. Manon is a simple country girl who falls in love with a nobleman, The Chevalier des Grieux, and runs away with him to Paris. Des Grieux's father objects to his son's choice of Manon, and also of their living together. He has his son abducted. Manon, a frivolous woman who is dazzled by jewelry and material wealth, had a chance to warn Des Grieux, but accepted the attention instead of a wealthy admirer who promised her riches. Dressed in high fashion and dripping in jewels, she is the center of attention at a popular elite carnival event in Paris. This is where she sings the aria, "Gavotte." Meanwhile, her first love, the heartbroken Des Grieux, has decided to enter the seminary and become a priest. Manon goes to him and rekindles their affair. Manon is later arrested for prostitution and sentenced to be deported to the French colony of Louisiana. She is in terrible health. Des Grieux bribes one of the guards to release Manon. She dies in Des Grieux's arms, hallucinating that she sees jewels before her — a frivolous woman to her death.

MANON LESCAUT (1893).

Music by Giacomo Puccini. Libretto by Marco Praga, Domenico Oliva, Giuseppe Giacosa, Luigi Illica. This opera is based on the same novel (by Abbé Prévost) as Massenet's *Manon*. The basic story line is the same (see *Manon* above). The aria "Donna non vidi mai" is sung by the tenor Des Grieux when he first sees Manon and is completely charmed by her. In Puccini's opera the last scene takes place "in the deserts of Louisiana" (certainly an uninformed French novelist's view). The Intermezzo is an orchestral interlude played between the scene of her banishment and the scene in Louisiana. Manon is indeed deported to the French colony, and Des Grieux accompanies her. They leave New Orleans and search for the British colony. At one point she finds herself alone in the wilderness, ill and exhausted, and she sings the dramatic aria, "Sola, perduta, abbandonata." Des Grieux returns to her, and she dies in his arms.

MARTHA (1847).

Music by Friedrich von Flotow. Libretto by Friedrich Wilhelm Riese. This opera was a favorite in the repertoire in the nineteenth century, but is a rarity today. It stays alive largely on the basis of a famous aria. The comic opera is set in England, c. 1710. Lady Harriet is bored, complaining to her maid/companion Nancy. They playfully disguise themselves as peasants and go to Richmond Fair, allowing themselves to be hired out as servants to two farmers, Lionel (the dashing one), and Plunkett (the more comic character). Harriet and Nancy fail completely to cook and clean adequately, but romance ensues between the faux-servants and the farmers. Lionel expresses his love for Martha in the aria "Ach, so fromm," better known in its Italian translation as "M'appari tutt'amor." The women escape. Lionel then finds out that he is the lost heir to the Earl of Derby, and inherits wealth and title. The couples reunite and all ends happily.

THE MERRY WIDOW (1905).

Music by Franz Lehár. This operetta started in Vienna as *Die Lustige Witwe*, and within two years it had swept Europe, and was playing in London and on Broadway. Several different English versions of the operetta have appeared over the years, including a film version that lyricist Lorenz Hart was forced to write for stars Jeanette MacDonald and Maurice Chevalier when he was under contract in Hollywood. (Hart hated the assignment.) The setting is Paris. A rich, young Pontevedrin widow, Hanna Glawari, is eager to fall in love again. After some operetta twists, she and the dashing Count Danilo wind up together. The show was revived on Broadway four times, the last being in 1943.

NORMA (1831).

Music by Vincenzo Bellini. Libretto by Felice Romani. This bel canto tragedy became closely identified with Maria Callas in the 1950s. The setting is Gaul during the Roman occupation, c. 50 B.C. Norma is a Druid high priestess, secretly married to the Roman Pollione. They have two sons. Pollione has lost interest in Norma and is now in love with Adalgisa. When Norma finds out about the affair she intends to kill herself, but Adalgisa persuades her to live. For a time, at least. Norma confesses that she is not a consecrated virgin, but is the mother of two sons. She sacrifices her life in a funeral pyre, and Pollione is moved to join her in death.

LE NOZZE DI FIGARO (The Marriage of Figaro) (1786).

Music by Wolfgang Amadeus Mozart. Libretto by Lorenzo da Ponte (adapted from the Beaumarchais play). The setting is 17th century Seville, though most productions play the opera in the 18th century. Figaro is valet to Count Almaviva. Susanna, Figaro's fiancé, is servant to Almaviva's wife, Countess Rosina. The Count wants to restore the "droit du seigneur" (rights of the lord), an old custom that allowed the nobleman the right to spend the wedding night with a bride from his estate before she was with her husband. The Count does everything to stall Figaro and Susanna's wedding, and employs the help of several lackeys. Cherubino is an adolescent, in love with all the ladies, and an annoyance to the Count. The philandering Count accuses his sweet, faithful wife, Rosina, of being unfaithful to him with the boy, Cherubino. Despite the Count's schemes, Figaro and Susanna are married, and in the end Almaviva begs his wife's forgiveness. "Porgi, amor" is sung by the Countess, as she laments being neglected by her husband. "Voi, che sapete" is a love song written by Cherubino, which he sings for the Countess and Susanna. "Deh vieni, non tardar" is sung by Susanna, in disguise as the Countess. She knows that her brand new husband (they were just married hours before), listens as she sings. "Contessa, perdono" is the Count's earnest plea for his wife's forgiveness.

ORFEO ED EURIDICE (Orpheus and Euridice) (1762).

Music by Christoph Willibald von Gluck. Libretto by Rainieri da Calzabigi (based on Greek myth). The setting is legendary Greece. Orfeo is the musician who laments of his beloved Euridice. Zeus takes pity on his grief and allows him to visit Hades. He may plead for her to return to life. But if she is allowed to follow him out of Hades he is forbidden to look back at her until they have emerged from the underworld. Euridice follows him, but is downhearted because Orfeo will not speak to her or look at her. She says she will go back if he continues to ignore her. He reluctantly looks back at her, and she fades back into Hades, forever lost to him. At this moment he sings the lament aria "Che farò senza Euridice." Orfeo is a "pants role," written for a mezzo-soprano.

I PAGLIACCI (The Clowns) (1892).

Music and libretto by Ruggero Leoncavallo. The opera is about a group of traveling players consisting of Canio (the leader), his wife, Nedda, and, a comic player, Tonio. Nedda has an affair with Silvio, and Tonio overhears them. He tells Canio of the adultery. That evening, before the comedy that he is to play, Canio sits before the makeup table, putting on his clown face. He is heartbroken, and sings the famous aria "Vesti la giubba." During the play he kills his wife, and then he kills Silvio. This short opera is often played on a double bill with *Cavalleria Rusticana*.

RIGOLETTO (1851).

Music by Giuseppe Verdi. Libretto by Francesco Piave. The opera takes place in Mantua, Italy, in the 16th century. Rigoletto is a hunchback jester in service to the Duke of Mantua. As the opera opens a ball is in progress in the Count's palace. He sings his philosophy about women in the aria "Questa o quella" (This one or that one, they're all the same to me). Count Monterone comes to the court and pleads for the honor of his daughter, who has been seduced by the Duke. Rigoletto ridicules Monterone, who curses him. The Duke disguises himself as a student and becomes enamored of Rigoletto's daughter, Gilda. She sings of her new love in the aria "Caro nome" (Dearest name). The Duke abducts Gilda. Rigoletto hires Sparafucile to murder the Duke in revenge. Maddalena, Sparafucile's sister, persuades him to spare the Duke and kill the first stranger who knocks at the door of the inn where they are staying, and provide Rigoletto with the cloaked body. It turns out to be Gilda who is murdered, and she dies in her father's arms as he screams, "the curse of Monterone!" The most famous tune in the opera is the Duke's aria, "La donna è mobile" (Woman is fickle, like a feather in the breeze).

LA RONDINE (The Swallow) (1917).

Music by Giacomo Puccini. Libretto by Giuseppe Adami. This light opera is a rarity in the repertoire. The setting is Paris during the Second Empire. Magda is mistress to the wealthy banker, Rambaldo. Act I takes place in a luxurious room in Magda's house, with many guests there for a party. One guest, Prunier sits at the piano and sings a song about a fictional Doretta, a simple girl who dreams that one day the King looks at her. Prunier cannot remember the end of the story. Magda remembers, and she sings this story of one Doretta in the aria "La Canzone di Doretta" (Chi'il bel sogno di Doretta). Magda is nostalgic for the simpler, innocent days of her past. Magda disguises herself as a maid and goes out in public, only to fall in love with Ruggero. She deserts Rambaldo and moves with Ruggero to Nice. But when Ruggero proposes marriage and wishes to introduce Magda to his mother, she decides she cannot pose as a virgin bride, sadly bids him farewell and returns to Paris.

SAMSON ET DALILA (Samson and Dalila) (1877).

Music by Camille Saint-Saëns. Libretto by Ferdinand Lemaire (based on the story in the Old Testament book of Judges). The opera takes place in Gaza, B.C. The Philistines, who worship the god Dagon, rule over the Israelites. Samson leads a rebellion against the rulers. Dalila, a Philistine, and Samson were once lovers. Urged by the High Priest of Dagon, she seduces Samson with the purpose of learning the secret of his strength. The aria "Mon cœur s'ouvre á ta voix" is Dalila's seduction. She succeeds, and learns that Samson's hair is the source for his strength. He is shorn and captured. Samson prays for one more burst of strength, and he destroys the Dagon temple, killing his foes and himself in the process.

SERSE (Xerxes) (1738).

Music by George Frideric Handel. Libretto by Niccolò Minato. The setting for this serio-comic Baroque opera is ancient Persia. King Xerxes is engaged to Amastre, but that doesn't stop him from being enchanted by the singing of Romilda, so enchanted that he falls in love with her. There are many plot twists, but Xerxes winds up with his original fiancé, Amastre in the end. "Ombra mai fù" is a very famous aria that is actually about very little. It's an ode to a stately tree. It is often called "Handel's Largo."

TANNHÄUSER (1845).

Music and libretto by Richard Wagner. The full title of this opera is *Tannhäuser und der Sängerkrieg auf Wartburg* (Tannhäuser and the Song Contest at the Wartburg). The story takes place in 13th century Germany in the Thuringian Valley. Tannhäuser is a knight and minstrel. He becomes fascinated with the voluptuous pleasures of the legendary Venusberg, a mountain inhabited by the goddess of love. His friend, Wolfram persuades him to return to Wartburg and his beloved Elisabeth, who is a niece of Hermann, the Landgrave (lord ruler) of Thuringia. Hermann holds a song contest, and the intent is that the winner wins the hand of Elisabeth. (He feels sure that Tannhäuser will win.) All the contestants are expected to sing idealistic songs of virtuous love, but Tannhäuser is impulsively seduced instead to sing of the sensual pleasures of the Venusberg. Everyone is horrified. Only Elisabeth defends him. Hermann allows that Tannhäuser will join a pilgrimage to Rome and plead for forgiveness from the Pope. Tannhäuser's friend Wolfram, in a scene alone in the evening, confesses that he too is in love with Elisabeth in the aria "O! du mein holder Abendstern" (The Evening Star). Elisabeth waits a long time for Tannhäuser's return, but when the pilgrims march in from their crusade (singing "Pilgrims' Chorus"), he is not among them, because the Pope has refused to grant him forgiveness. Elisabeth dies of a broken heart. When Tannhäuser sees Elisabeth's coffin, he himself dies. Another band of pilgrims arrive, carrying Tannhäuser's staff, which now is in bloom, a sign that he has been forgiven.

THAÏS (1894).

Music by Jules Massenet. Libretto by Louis Gallet. The opera takes place in the fourth century, A.D., in and near Alexandria, Egypt. Athanaël is a monk who attempts to save the soul of the courtesan Thaïs. He succeeds in convincing her to leave her life of luxury and enter a convent, but in the process of his persuasion, he falls in love with her. In a dream he sees her purified by sincere repentance, but ill and dying. Athanaël goes to her, and indeed finds Thaïs near death. While he wants to profess his love for her and hold her, she is in religious ecstasy, and sees a vision of heaven. The "Meditation" is an instrumental interlude between acts.

TOSCA (1900).
Music by Giacomo Puccini. Libretto by Giuseppe Giacosa and Luigi Illica (adapted from the play by Sardou). The setting for this famous melodrama is Rome, c. 1800. Mario Cavaradossi is a painter in love with Floria Tosca, a famous singer. He is working on a mural in the Church of Sant' Andrea della Valle, and sings the aria "Recondita armonia," comparing the face in the portrait he is painting to Tosca. Cavaradossi offers help to Angelotti, an escaped political prisoner who is an activist in the movement to make Rome a democratic republic. The hypocritical and tyrannical Scarpia is chief of police, the man who sent Angelotti to prison. Scarpia is also in love with Tosca. Cavaradossi agrees to hide Angelotti at his house. Scarpia arrests Cavaradossi and interrogates him, then has him tortured in an effort to obtain information about Angelotti's whereabouts. Tosca pleads with Scarpia to show mercy to Cavaradossi, but the torture continues, which Tosca can hear coming from the floor below. To stop the torture to her lover, Tosca reluctantly tells Scarpia Angelotti's hiding place, despite Cavaradossi's previous pleas to her to say nothing, no matter what. Scarpia signs a death warrant for Cavaradossi's execution. Scarpia tells Tosca that if she gives herself to him he will spare her lover's life. In a moment of desperation she sings the prayer-aria "Vissi d'arte." Tosca agrees to Scarpia's deal. He says a mock execution must be staged, then Cavaradossi and Tosca can flee. She sees a knife on the table, and before Scarpia makes love to her she stabs and kills him. Meanwhile, Cavaradossi is in prison, expecting to die at dawn, and sings the poignant aria "E lucevan le stelle" as he remembers Tosca and their love. Tosca enters and tells him of Scarpia's death, and the mock execution plan. As Cavaradossi lies there after the firing squad has shot at him (Tosca believes the bullets are blanks), Tosca suddenly realizes that her lover is actually dead. At that moment Scarpia's murder is discovered, and Tosca runs to the edge of the tower and jumps off, killing herself.

LA TRAVIATA (The Straying One, or The Fallen Woman) (1853).
Music by Giuseppe Verdi. Libretto by Francesco Piave (adapted from the play *La Dame aux Camelias* by Alexandre Dumas). The setting is Paris, c. 1850. Violetta is a beautiful courtesan. Alfredo Germont, who has fallen in love with her from afar, is at a party at her house and leads everyone in "Libiamo," a drinking song to pleasure. Violetta is at first disbelieving of Alfredo's profession of love for her, but is deeply moved. They leave Paris and live together in a country house outside the city. Alfredo's father, who disapproves of his son's illicit relationship, comes to persuade Violetta to end the romance so that his family honor can be restored. He tells Violetta that his daughter is engaged to a young man from a noble family. Germont fears that the fiancé's family will find out about Alfredo's immorality and refuse to allow the marriage. After heartbreaking conflict she agrees to give Alfredo up. She writes a letter to him. The elder Germont is on hand when Alfredo reads it, and he tries to console his son in the aria "Di provenza." Alfredo is bitter. In Paris again, Violetta becomes gravely ill from consumption. Facing the reality of her sure death she sings the tragic aria "Addio, del passatto." Alfredo discovers the truth about her sacrifice and their break-up and comes to her again. But it is too late. She lives just long enough for the two to renew their love for one another.

IL TROVATORE (The Troubadour) (1853).
Music by Giuseppe Verdi. Libretto by Salvatore Cammarano. The opera takes place in 15th century Spain. It has one of the most confusing plots of any piece in the standard repertoire. Count di Luna and Manrico are enemies in a civil war. They do not know that they are actually brothers. They both love the Duchess Leonora. Azucena is a gypsy woman. She and Manrico are imprisoned by Count di Luna. Leonora loves Manrico, and offers herself to di Luna in exchange for Manrico's freedom. Di Luna agrees, but Leonora has no intention of giving herself to the Count, and she secretly takes poison. Leonora goes to Manrico to tell him he is free, but when the Count sees her dying he orders Manrico to be beheaded. Long ago Azucena's mother was burned at the stake by Count di Luna's father. When Azucena sees Manrico's murder, she reveals that he has killed his own brother, and by this tragedy her mother's cruel death has been avenged. The "Anvil Chorus" is sung by gypsies at work in their camp at night. In the same scene is Azucena's aria "Stride la vampa," in which she describes her mother's horrible death.

LA WALLY (1892).
Music by Alfredo Catalani. Libretto by Luigi Illica. This is one of the operas that is hardly ever produced, and is only known for one famous aria. The opera takes place in the Austrian Tyrol, c. 1800. The old man Stromminger is enemies with Hagenbach and his father. Though she did not know his identity, Wally, Stromminger's daughter, has been secretly in love with Hagenbach for years. Stromminger insists that Wally marry Gellner. But Stromminger dies, and Wally, still unmarried, inherits a fortune. Hagenbach, meanwhile becomes engaged to Afra. Wally becomes furious at that news and insults Hagenbach's fiancé, which Hagenbach swears to avenge. Wally is hurt by Hagenbach and asks Gellner to kill him. She later regrets this wish, but Gellner has already pushed Hagenbach off a cliff. He survives, and Wally reunites him with Afra. Wally is lonely and sad and wanders in the mountains. Hagenbach comes to find her to profess his love for her. Hagenbach leaves temporarily to scout the path ahead, and in his absence Wally, not feeling worthy of his love for her because she tried to kill him, throws herself into an avalanche. (You can see why the opera is rarely done.) The aria "Ebben, n'andro lontana" was prominently used in the film *Diva*, and also has been heard in television commercials.

DIE ZAUBERFLÖTE (The Magic Flute) (1791).

Music by Wolfgang Amadeus Mozart. Libretto by Emmanuel Schikaneder. This is a fairytale opera, although it's admittedly an unusual fairytale. The setting is legendary Egypt, although productions of the opera are often set in an unspecified locale. Prince Tamino is being chased by a giant serpent. Three ladies, in service to the Queen of the Night, slay the dragon and save his life. The Queen's bird-catcher, an odd and comic fellow himself covered with bird feathers, enters and sings his entrance song ("Papageno's Song"), introducing himself to the audience. The three ladies show Tamino a portrait of the Queen of the Night's daughter, Pamina, and he immediately and idealistically falls in love with her, sight unseen. The Queen of the Night asks him to rescue Pamina from Sarastro, whom she describes as an evil sorcerer. As Tamino and Papageno leave they are given a set of magic bells and a magic flute, which cast spells that will protect them. They are also given three young spirits as companions. In Sarastro's temple to the god Isis, Tamino learns the evil truth about the Queen of the Night, and is persuaded of Sarastro's goodness and idealism. The Queen of the Night appears in Sarastro's domain, and is completely furious, demanding that Pamina kill Sarastro with a dagger. She then sings the "Vengeance Aria" ("Der Hölle Rache kocht in meinem Herzen"), which boils with fire. The coloratura vocal line ascends to a strastopheric high F above high C four times. (Mozart wrote the role to accomodate the unusual range of the original singer who portrayed the Queen of the Night.) Tamino commits to become a member of Sarastro's brotherhood. As part of the initiation, Tamino and Papageno are ordered not to speak. Pamina then comes to Tamino, and she believes his silence is because he no longer loves her. She then sings the sad aria, "Ach, ich fühl's." The heroic Tamino completes his trials, and Sarastro blesses his union with Pamina. Papageno is also rewarded (even though he is incapable of completing the trials because of his feebleness) with a mate, Papagena. The Queen of the Night and her attendants fail in their attempt to seize Sarastro's temple, and are taken to hell. Sarastro presides over the triumph of goodness and light.

Triumphal March
AÏDA

Giuseppe Verdi
1813-1901

Allegro moderato

Celeste Aïda
AÏDA

Giuseppe Verdi
1813-1901

Andantino (♪ = 116)

Una voce poco fa

IL BARBIERE DI SIVIGLIA
(The Barber of Seville)

Gioachino Rossini
1792-1868

Che gelida manina

LA BOHÈME
(The Bohemian Life)

Giacomo Puccini
1858-1924

Slowly

O soave fanciulla

LA BOHÈME
(The Bohemian Life)

Giacomo Puccini
1858-1924

Largo sostenuto (♩ = 58)

Quando men vo
(Musetta's Waltz)
LA BOHÈME
(The Bohemian Life)

Giacomo Puccini
1858-1924

Sono andati

LA BOHÈME
(The Bohemian Life)

Giacomo Puccini
1858-1924

Habanera
CARMEN

Georges Bizet
1838-1875

Seguidilla

CARMEN

Georges Bizet
1838-1875

Flower Song
CARMEN

Georges Bizet
1838-1875

Andantino

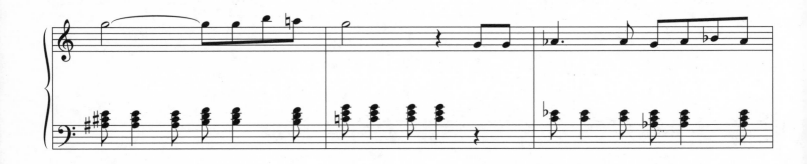

Toreador Song

CARMEN

Georges Bizet
1838-1875

Allegro moderato

Barcarolle

LES CONTES D'HOFFMANN
(The Tales of Hoffmann)

Jacques

Intermezzo
CAVALLERIA RUSTICANA

Pietro Mascagni
1863-1945

When I am laid in earth
DIDO AND ÆNEAS

Henry Purcell
1659-1695

Vedrai, carino
DON GIOVANNI

Wolfgang Amadeus Mozart
1756-1791

Là ci darem la mano

DON GIOVANNI

Wolfgang Amadeus Mozart
1756-1791

Minuet
DON GIOVANNI

Wolfgang Amadeus Mozart
1756-1791

63

Una furtiva lagrima

L'ELISIR D'AMORE
(The Elixir of Love)

Gaetano Donizetti
1797-1848

Larghetto

65

For Leva

Lenski's Aria
EUGENE ONEGIN

Pyotr Il'yich Tchaikovsky
1840-1893

Poco più animato

Andante mosso

Salut! demeure chaste et pure

FAUST

Charles Gounod
1818-1893

Spirto gentil

LA FAVORITA
(The Favorite Woman)

Gaetano Donizetti
1797-1848

76

Amor ti vieta
FEDORA

Umberto Giordano
1867-1948

Sostenuto (♪ = 126)

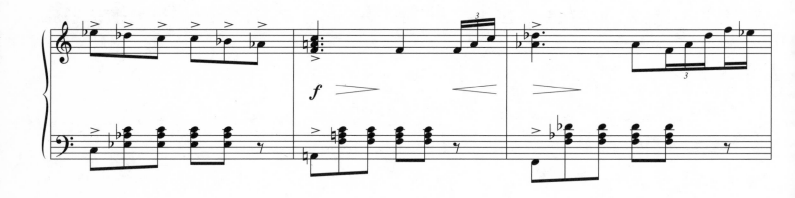

Andante cantabile (♩ = 54)

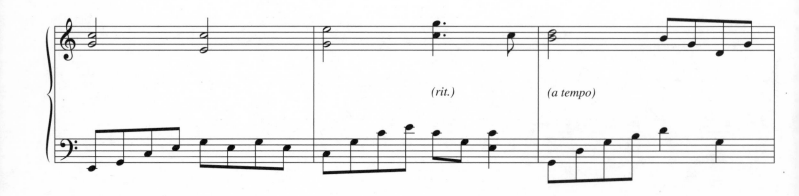

The Fledermaus Waltz

DIE FLEDERMAUS
(The Bat)

Johann Strauss, Jr.
1825-1899

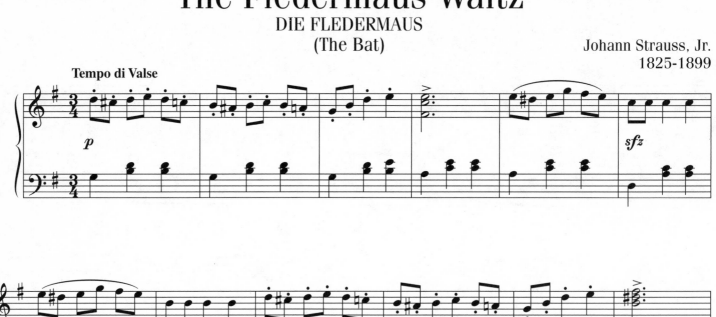

Chacun à son goût

DIE FLEDERMAUS
(The Bat)

Johann Strauss, Jr.
1825-1899

Allegro non troppo

O mio babbino caro

GIANNI SCHICCHI

Giacomo Puccini
1858-1924

Andante ingenuo

Rinuccio's Aria
(Firenze è come un alberto fiorito)
GIANNI SCHICCHI

Giacomo Puccini
1858-1924

Andante mosso un po' sostenuto

Andante sostenuto

**Come il tempo primo
(Andante mosso)**

Un po' sostenuto

Piangerò la sorte mia

GIULIO CESARE
(Julius Caesar)

George Frideric Handel
1685-1759

93

(Adagio)

D.C. al Fine

HMS PINAFORE

Selected Melodies

Arthur Sullivan
1842-1900

Allegro
"We Sail the Ocean Blue"

Andante
"Sorry Her Lot"

Poco animato

Allegretto
"I'm Called Little Buttercup"

Allegretto
"I am the Captain of the Pinafore"

Maestoso
"For He is an Englishman"

William Tell Overture

GUILLAUME TELL
(William Tell)

Gioachino Rossini
1792-1868

Evening Prayer
HÄNSEL UND GRETEL

Engelbert Humperdinck
1854-1921

Adagio

Berceuse
JOCELYN

Benjamin Godard
1849-1895

Sextet
(Chi raffrena il mio furore)
LUCIA DI LAMMERMOOR

Gaetano Donizetti
1797-1848

Larghetto

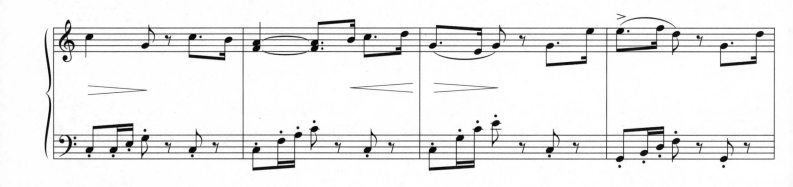

Depuis le jour
LOUISE

Gustave Charpentier
1860-1956

Un poco animato (♩ = 72)

Entrance of Butterfly

MADAMA BUTTERFLY

Giacomo Puccini
1858-1924

Largo

122

Addio, fiorito asil
MADAMA BUTTERFLY

Giacomo Puccini
1858-1924

Un bel dì vedremo

MADAMA BUTTERFLY

Giacomo Puccini
1858-1924

Andante molto calmo

Gavotte
MANON

Jules Massenet
1842-1912

Moderato e leggero

Moderato e leggero

Donna non vidi mai

MANON LESCAUT

Giacomo Puccini
1858-1924

Andante lento

Sola, perduta, abbandonata

MANON LESCAUT

Giacomo Puccini
1858-1924

Largo molto sostenuto

Molto sostenuto

Intermezzo

MANON LESCAUT

Giacomo Puccini
1858-1924

138

M'appari tutt'amor
(Ach, so fromm)
MARTHA

Friedrich von Flotow
1812-1883

THE MERRY WIDOW
Selected Melodies

Franz Lehár
1870-1948

Allegretto moderato

"Silly Cavalier"

Tempo di Valse Lente
"The Merry Widow Waltz"

Tempo di Valse

Waltz from Finale, Act I

sfz *a piacere*

rall.

p

pp delicato
a tempo

Più Allegro

150

Andantino
"Vilia"

con molto espressivo

p a tempo

Allegro
"The Study of Woman"

Casta diva
NORMA

Vincenzo Bellini
1802-1835

Andante sostenuto assai

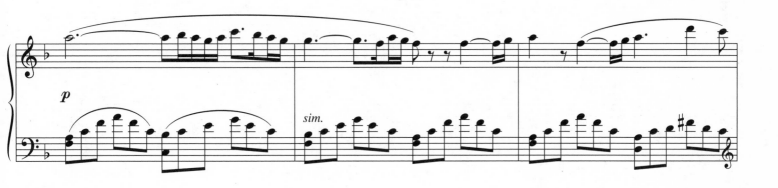

Porgi, amor

LE NOZZE DI FIGARO
(The Marriage of Figaro)

Wolfgang Amadeus Mozart
1756-1791

Larghetto

Voi, che sapete

LE NOZZE DI FIGARO
(The Marriage of Figaro)

Wolfgang Amadeus Mozart
1756-1791

Andante con moto

Deh vieni, non tardar

LE NOZZE DI FIGARO
(The Marriage of Figaro)

Wolfgang Amadeus Mozart
1756-1791

Contessa, perdono

LE NOZZE DI FIGARO
(The Marriage of Figaro)

Wolfgang Amadeus Mozart
1756-1791

Vesti la giubba

I PAGLIACCI
(The Clowns)

Ruggero Leoncavallo
1857-1919

Che farò senza Euridice?

ORFEO ED EURIDICE

Christoph von Gluck
1714-1787

Allegretto

Tempo I

172

Mon cœur s'ouvre á ta voix
SAMSON ET DALILA

Camille Saint-Saëns
1834-1921

Caro nome
RIGOLETTO

Giuseppe Verdi
1813-1901

Allegro moderato

freely

a tempo dolce

Questa o quella
RIGOLETTO

Giuseppe Verdi
1813-1901

Allegretto

La donna è mobile
RIGOLETTO

Giuseppe Verdi
1813-1901

La Canzone di Doretta

(Chi il bel sogno di Doretta)
LA RONDINE

Giacomo Puccini
1858-1924

Ombra mai fù

SERSE
(Xerxes)

George Frideric Handel
1685-1759

The Evening Star
TANNHÄUSER

Richard Wagner
1813-1883

Moderato

Pilgrims' Chorus

TANNHÄUSER

Richard Wagner
1813-1883

Andante maestoso

Meditation
THAÏS

Jules Massenet
1842-1912

Recondita armonia

TOSCA

Giacomo Puccini
1858-1924

Andante lento

Più lento

Più lento

Vissi d'arte
TOSCA

Giacomo Puccini
1858-1924

Andante lento appassionato

E lucevan le stelle

TOSCA

Giacomo Puccini
1858-1924

Lento, appassionato molto

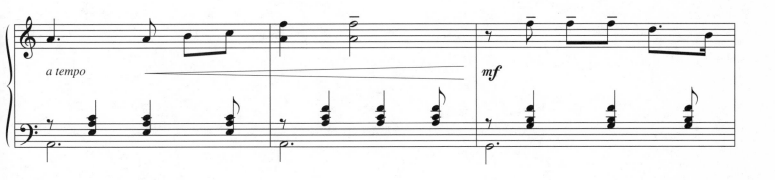

Ebben, n'andrò lontana

LA WALLY

Alfredo Catalani
1854-1893

Andante molto sostenuto
con molto sentimento

Tempo I

Libiamo
LA TRAVIATA
(The Fallen Woman)

Giuseppe Verdi
1813-1901

Di provenza il mar, il suol

LA TRAVIATA
(The Fallen Woman)

Giuseppe Verdi
1813-1901

Andante piuttosto mosso

Addio, del passatto

LA TRAVIATA
(The Fallen Woman)

Giuseppe Verdi
1813-1901

Andante mosso

Anvil Chorus
IL TROVATORE
(The Troubadour)

Giuseppe Verdi
1813-1901

Stride la vampa
IL TROVATORE
(The Troubadour)

Giuseppe Verdi
1813-1901

Dies Bildnis ist bezaubernd schön

DIE ZAUBERFLÖTE
(The Magic Flute)

Wolfgang Amadeus Mozart
1756-1791

Papageno's Song

DIE ZAUBERFLÖTE
(The Magic Flute)

Wolfgang Amadeus Mozart
1756-1791

Ach, ich fühl's

DIE ZAUBERFLÖTE
(The Magic Flute)

Wolfgang Amadeus Mozart
1756-1791

Andante

Queen of the Night's Vengeance Aria

DIE ZAUBERFLÖTE
(The Magic Flute)

Wolfgang Amadeus Mozart
1756-1791

Allegro assai